CHARLIE BROWN
P-M

VIOLET
I²

SHERMY
IB

PATTY
F

SCHROEDER
C

SNOOPY
SS

LINUS
2B

LUCY
CF

'PIG-PEN'
3B

THE WONDERFUL

WORLD OF

PEANUTS®

Selected Cartoons From
more PEANUTS.
VOL 1

by Charles M. Schulz

A FAWCETT CREST BOOK

Fawcett Publications, Inc., Greenwich, Conn.

Member of American Book Publishers Council, Inc.

THE WONDERFUL WORLD OF PEANUTS

This book, prepared especially for Fawcett Publications, Inc., comprises the first half of MORE PEANUTS, and is reprinted by arrangement with Holt, Rinehart and Winston, Inc.

Fourteenth Fawcett Crest printing, June 1968

Published by Fawcett World Library,
67 West 44th Street, New York, N. Y. 10036
Printed in the United States of America

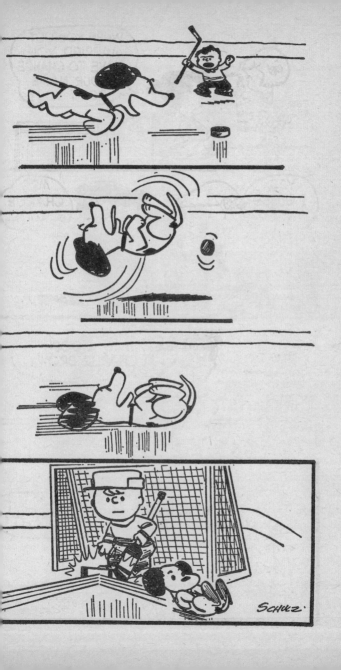

ARE YOU GOING TO NURSERY SCHOOL THESE DAYS, LUCY?

YES, I'VE BEEN REINSTATED

IS IT FUN?

IS IT FUN?! ALL WE HAVE TO DO EVERY DAY IS PLAY PLAY PLAY PLAY PLAY PLAY...

I'VE NEVER BEEN SO BORED IN ALL MY LIFE!

SCHULZ.

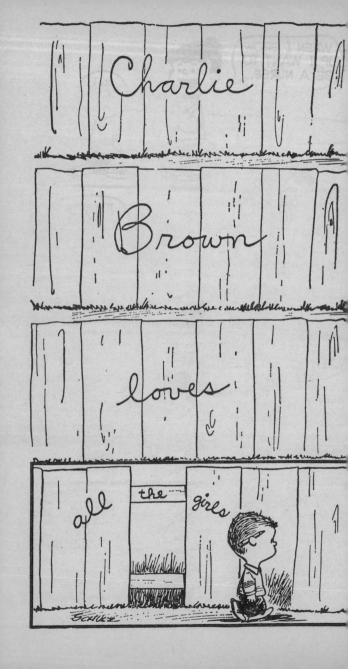

SHERMY!

SHERMY